Richie and Shelly
at the Farm Festival
an Adventure in Healthy Eating

Written by
Cathy Macri

Illustrated by
Theresa Stites

There are many people to thank who have been role models and healthy eating advocates, but I especially want to thank my daughter, Lauren, whose passion for eating healthy, organic foods inspired this Richie and Shelly book.

Richie and Shelly
at the Farm Festival
an Adventure in Healthy Eating

Written by
Cathy Macri

Eat Your Veggies!

Cathy Macri

Illustrated by
Theresa Stites

"Hurry, Shelly," called Richie as he ran from the bus to school.

"What's the rush?" asked Shelly as she tried to catch up to her older brother.

"Today is the Annual Farm Festival," he replied.

"What's a Farm Festival?" asked Shelly. This was Shelly's first year at Green Meadow School.

Richie knew everything about school.

"It's when Farmer Brown visits the school. He tells us about eating fresh fruit and vegetables and brings some from his farm for all of us to taste," Richie called back to her.

"Yummy, I love vegetables!" shouted Shelly running behind him.

Shelly's teacher, Mrs. Witt, explained even more about the Farm Festival.

"Farmer Brown owns the big farm on the other side of the hill. Each year he brings fresh fruit and vegetables for all of us to enjoy. There are stands in the field where some of your parents will tell you about the food. Then, you'll even get to taste them!"

The children were all very excited and could hardly wait their turn to go outside.

Farmer Brown and his dog, Tater, greeted the children as they sat on the grass. He asked if they all liked vegetables and they were all very enthusiastic as each told Farmer Brown what their favorite vegetable was.

Farmer Brown told them about all the fruit and vegetables he grows on his farm.

"All my vegetables are organic. I use only natural ingredients to fertilize my crops and help the plants grow and keep away pests. It is very important to eat the healthiest foods. At each meal, half of your plate should be fruit and vegetables. They contain vitamins that help you grow strong and healthy."

Shelly listened closely to how Farmer Brown plants seeds each spring to harvest in the summer and fall. She thought she might like to try to grow vegetables. She'd be sure to give them plenty of sun and water, just like Farmer Brown does with his plants.

Shelly knew that Richie's favorite part of Farmer Brown's speech would be about the farm equipment. He even showed the children one of the tractors he brought with him! Everyone had a chance to climb on the tractor and pretend they were the farmers. What fun!

The children all thanked Farmer Brown
as they moved to the first vegetable
stand to get a taste of green beans.

Mrs. Hughes, Nina's mother, spoke about green beans. She told the children that green beans have lots of B vitamins to keep their bodies growing strong and healthy. Then Mrs. Hughes passed out samples of the beans to the children. "These are delicious!" exclaimed Shelly, smiling at Nina. All her classmates agreed. They all thanked Mrs. Hughes as they moved on to the next stand.

There were stands with tomatoes, squash, broccoli, corn, apples, and lots of other good things. The children got to taste each one and learn about all the vitamins they were getting.

By now, Richie and his class had come onto the field. Richie shook Farmer Brown's hand and told him how much he liked vegetables.

Farmer Brown was glad to hear it. He invited the boys and girls to visit the farm any time.

"And can we ride the tractor?" asked Richie.

"Yes," said Farmer Brown smiling, "and ride the tractor."

Zucchini
Broccoli
Cabbage

All the classes returned to their rooms
and discussed what they had learned.
The children learned so much that day
and in a most delicious way!

When it was lunchtime, they were all treated to a fresh garden salad and vegetable soup made with onions, carrots, celery, squash, and tomatoes.

They also had fresh apple juice and apples for dessert...all from Farmer Brown's farm.

When Richie and Shelly got home that day, they couldn't wait to tell their mother about Farmer Brown and his delicious fruits and vegetables.

"Great," said Mom, "because I'm making chicken and my special acorn squash and roasted red potatoes for dinner!"

"My favorites," Richie and Shelly said at the same time. Everyone laughed and then Richie and Shelly told Mom all about the important vitamins in their dinner. Mom was glad to hear about their day.

That evening while they were enjoying their chicken and squash, Richie told Mom and Dad about Farmer Brown's invitation to visit the farm.

"Can we go?" he asked.

"It sounds like a fun day," said Dad. "Maybe we will."

Green Meadow School Beef Vegetable Soup

- 1 lb. lean ground beef (optional)
- 1 cup chopped onion
- 1 cup chopped celery
- 1 cup chopped carrots
- 1 cup peeled chopped green squash
- 2 cloves garlic, minced
- 1 lb. peeled and diced tomatoes
- 15 oz. homemade tomato sauce or 15 oz. can tomato sauce
- 2 19 oz. cans kidney beans, drained and rinsed
- 2 cups water (low sodium organic beef broth can be used)
- 1 tbsp. fresh chopped or dried parsley
- ½ tsp fresh chopped or dried oreganov
- ½ tsp fresh chopped or dried basil
- 2 cups chopped cabbage
- 15 oz. corn kernels or 1 can whole kernel corn
- 1 cup small macaroni (ditalini, small shells, elbows, orzo, etc.)

Place ground beef in large soup pot. Cook over medium heat until evenly browned. Drain fat. Stir in onion, celery, carrots, garlic, diced tomatoes, tomato sauce, beans, and water (or broth). Season with parsley, oregano, and basil. Simmer 25 minutes. Stir in cabbage, corn, and green squash. Bring to boil and then reduce heat. Simmer until all vegetables are tender. Add more water if too thick. Cook pasta separately until al dente. Add pasta to soup last five minutes. If you like you can serve with a warm loaf of crusty Italian or French bread.

Use home-grown or organic vegetables when possible for the healthiest soup!

This is a very thick and hearty soup!

The End

Dear Parents,

I have written this book about Richie and Shelly and healthy eating because I feel this is an important topic. I encourage you to use this book to have discussions with your children about what they eat and the importance of healthy eating and making healthy choices when shopping. I have included a recipe at the end of the book and suggest you include your children when cooking healthy foods to nurture their interest.

Thank you for reading this book. Watch for future Richie and Shelly books as they continue their adventures in healthy eating!

Cathy Macri